The Whale's Year

Written by Christine Butterworth

Contents

Introduction

Blue whales are the biggest animals in the world. They live in the sea.

This book tells you about a year
in the life of a blue whale.

The blue whale stays in warm water in winter.

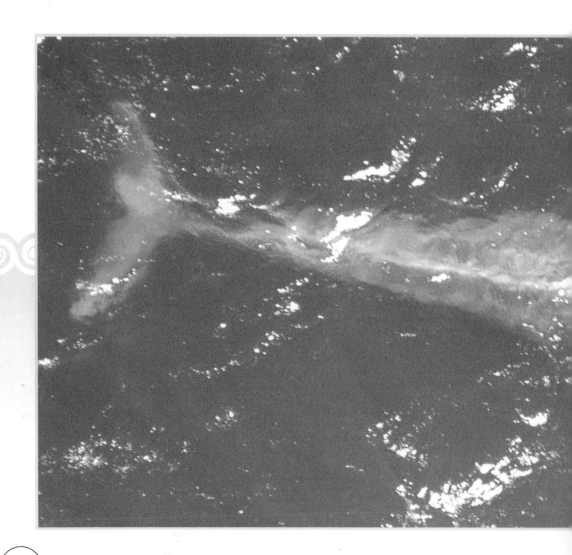

Soon the whale will have a baby.

Spring

The whale has had her baby.
A baby whale is called a calf.

The calf drinks about 365 litres of its mother's milk each day. That's over one thousand glasses of milk!

calf

mother

Summer

The whale eats most of her food in summer. She swims a long way to find cold water. There is a lot of food there.

She sucks in water and tiny sea animals called krill.

krill

Autumn

Summer ends, and it is time for the mother and calf to go back to warm water.

The whales make noises as they swim. They 'sing' to each other.

Winter again

The whales are back in warm water.
Soon the calf will be a year old.

It is time for the calf to leave
its mother.

Through the year

Winter	Spring
Blue whales stay in warm waters	The baby whales are born

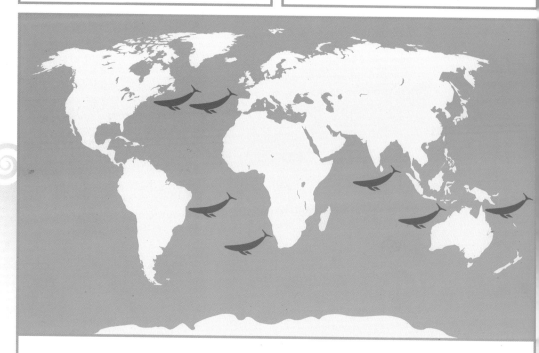

The whales are in warm waters.

Summer	Autumn
They feed in cold waters	They swim back to warm waters

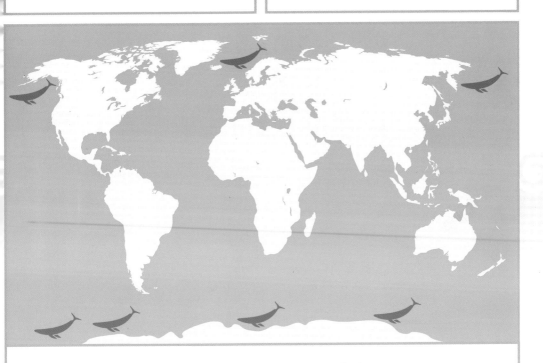

The whales are in cold waters.

Index

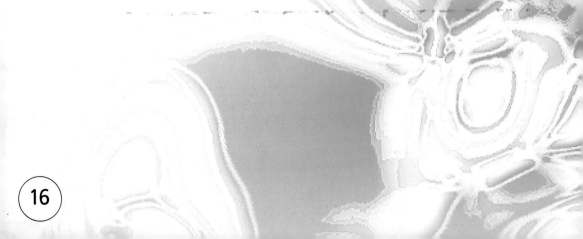